D0418655

THE BOY WHO ASKED FOR 'MORE'

The Story of Charles Dickens

James Riordan

Illustrated by
Kay Dixey

an imprint of Hodder Children's Books

Charles Dickens

Charles Dickens was born on 7 February 1812 in a narrow terraced house in Portsmouth. His grandparents had been servants and his father worked in the Navy Pay Office.

Dickens lived during the Industrial Revolution, a time when most people moved from the country into towns to work in factories. There were terrible conditions in the factories where children as young as five were often forced to work – sometimes thirteen hours a day, six days a week. Those who could not support themselves were made to live and work in the workhouse. Prisons were overcrowded with criminals and families that had fallen into debt.

When Charles was twelve, most of his family went to prison for his father's debts. Charles had to work in a London warehouse.

From these humble beginnings, Dickens became one of the world's greatest writers. Through his books, readers can begin to understand what it must have been like to live in Victorian times.

When he died on 9 June 1870, Charles Dickens was buried in Poets' Corner, Westminster Abbey. His books continue to be read and loved by readers of all ages.

Charles Dickens' best known novels:

1837	*The Pickwick Papers*
1838	*Oliver Twist*
1839	*Nicholas Nickleby*
1845	*A Christmas Carol*
1850	*David Copperfield*
1857	*Little Dorrit*
1859	*A Tale of Two Cities*
1860	*Great Expectations*

Chapter 1

David lay curled up before the blazing fire. With a sigh, he shut his book, making a noise that woke his grandfather.

"Sorry, Grandad. It was *Oliver Twist* that woke you up." David had just finished reading one of Charles Dickens' stories. The words 'Oliver Twist' startled his grandad.

"Did you enjoy it, David?" he asked.

"Very much, Dickens is my favourite author," David said, staring into the crackling fire. "Were children's lives really so hard in those days, Grandad?"

The old man smiled. He had never told David his secret. Perhaps now was the time.

"They were hard times all right," he began. "I'll tell you about them if you like. You see, *Oliver Twist* is a very special story to me, too..."

... Fifty years ago, when I was ten, I went to prison for something I didn't do. I was forced to do three months of hard work in Marshalsea Gaol. It was a truly terrible place surrounded by a high, spiked wall.

I was sitting in my freezing-cold cell
one day when I heard someone tapping on
the wall. Then I heard a whisper. It was a
gentleman by the name of John Dickens,
a debtor:

Well, the next day, his wife and four young children moved into the prison as well. Imagine! Six of them living in a tiny cell with one iron bed. The family had high hopes for their son, Charley, to earn enough money to save them. He was working ten hours a day at a warehouse by the River Thames. It was overrun with big grey rats. Charley's job was to paste labels on to paint pots.

Since I had heard so much about him,
and he was about my age, I was looking
forward to meeting Master Dickens.

Chapter 2

Next Sunday afternoon, Charley Dickens arrived at the prison with his fourteen-year-old sister, Fanny. She was studying at the Royal College of Music. Charley had walked all the way from Camden Town where he lived alone in a draughty attic room. He was tall for his age – twelve – with a large head topped by curly chestnut hair. He seemed to be a rather quiet boy.

After an hour or so with his family, he came out into the prison yard and we got chatting. He asked me why I was in prison, so I told him my story…

I was born in a workhouse in 1814. Because of this start, my nickname had become 'Work'ouse'; I had no other name. You see, I was an orphan. They say that I breathed, sneezed and gave a loud cry; then my poor mother kissed me with her cold, white lips – and fell back and died.

No one knew who she was or where
she came from, and there was no ring
on her finger.

So there I was, left in the workhouse,
fed on sevenpence-halfpenny-worth of
food that the Poor Law allowed. No
wonder I was so pale and skinny.

When I was nine, the beadle, a fat, sweaty man called Mr Bumble, put me to work picking oakum with the older boys. We worked hard from six in the morning until eight at night. They fed us three meals of watery gruel a day, an onion twice a week and half a roll on Sundays. It was the food that got me into trouble in the end.

Chapter 3

Whe ate all our meals in a large stone hall with a big pot of gruel at one end. As each boy went up for food, the master spooned gruel into his bowl. Believe me, those bowls never needed washing – we practically licked them clean! Then we'd sit staring at the pot. We were starving.

One day, a boy said that he was so hungry that he might eat the boy sleeping next to him. He looked so sick with hunger that we believed him. We decided then that something had to be done. So we drew lots and it fell to me to go up and ask for more food.

The next mealtime, we all took our
places at the long table in the hall. The
master served out the gruel and, as usual,
the gruel quickly disappeared. Some of the
boys started winking and whispering at
me, and my neighbour dug me in the ribs.

Slowly I took my spoon and bowl and
went up to the master.

Please, Sir,
I want some more.

The master was a fat, red-faced man, yet suddenly he turned pale and had to hold on to the pot for support. The room was so silent that you could have heard the rats breathing.

Finally, the master said faintly, "What?"

"Please, Sir, I want some more," I said again. That did it. The master hit me over the head with the big gruel spoon and shouted for Mr Bumble, who came and locked me away.

The next morning they stuck a notice on the workhouse gate offering five pounds to anyone who would take me off their hands.

Chapter 4

Before long, I got taken on as an apprentice to the local undertaker. My new owner, Mr Sowerberry, a tall, thin man dressed entirely in black, came to pick me up from the workhouse.

As we were leaving, Mr Bumble shouted a warning to me, "If you ever come back to the workhouse, Work'ouse, we'll send you to sea to be drowned!"

My new bed was a mattress beneath a wall of coffins. It was really scary at night, when the coffins looked like ghosts in the dark.

Because of all the illness around, the funeral business was doing well at the time. The only trouble was that I was bullied by an older boy who worked there, too. He was called Noah Claypole, and he was a big boy with small, unfriendly eyes. One day, Noah went too far. "Work'ouse," he said. "How's your mother?"

I replied that she had passed away.

"What did she die of, Work'ouse?" Noah asked.

"Of a broken heart," I said.

"Just as well she's dead," he continued, "or she'd have been hung by now. She must've been a bad'un."

I lost my temper at that. Even though he was twice my size, I grabbed Noah by the throat and shook him until his teeth chattered. Then I hit him so hard that he fell to the floor, screaming loudly.

Of course, I got the blame. But before the undertaker, his wife and Noah could get hold of me, I decided to run away – as far away as possible.

I walked twenty miles on the first day, tasting nothing but a crust of bread and a few drops of water I had begged at cottage doors. As I sat down to rest at the roadside, I noticed a milestone which said: 'London 70 miles'. *London*! That was a big place. Nobody, not even Mr Bumble would find me there.

Chapter 5

On the seventh day of walking, I reached London and soon met one of the strangest-looking boys I had ever seen. He was about my age, but shorter with bow legs. He had little sharp eyes and the dirtiest face imaginable. Most unusually, the boy was wearing a dusty old top-hat.

When I told him, he said, "I know a
'spectable ol' gentleman who'll give you
a room in London for nothin'."

The boy's name was Jack Dawkins, though he said that he was better known as the Artful Dodger. The part of London he took me to was poor and filthy. We climbed some dark, broken stairs and entered a room at the back of a house. The walls were black with dirt. Seated around a table were four or five boys smoking long clay pipes and drinking beer like men.

Above them was a clothes line full of silk handkerchiefs. In front of the fire, cooking sausages on a toasting fork, was a very old man whose face was covered by long matted red hair.

"This, Fagin, is my new friend, Work'ouse," said the Dodger.

"We are all very glad to meet you, Work'ouse," said the old fellow, turning to look at me.

And at that, we all sat down to supper.

Chapter 6

The next day, after breakfast, Fagin and two of the boys started playing a very strange game. Fagin put a snuffbox and hankie in one of his trouser pockets, a wallet in the other, a watch in his waistcoat pocket and a glasses case inside his jacket. Then he trotted up and down the room with a walking stick, just like a rich man. He kept glancing round in fear of thieves. It was such a funny sight that I laughed until the tears ran down my face.

All the while, the two boys were
following him about. If Fagin felt a hand in
any of his pockets, he'd shout out and the
game would end. At last, the Dodger trod
on his toes and the other lad bumped into
him from behind. In that moment they
took his snuffbox, wallet, watch, silk
hankie, even his spectacles case.

Finally, the Dodger said, "Time to pad the hoof," which meant going outside into the streets. I was invited to join them.

As we were walking down the high
street, the two boys crept up behind an
old gentleman. In a flash, the Dodger stole
a hankie from his back pocket and ran
off quickly.

Of course, the whole mystery of the clothes line, the pick-pocket games and Jack's nickname was becoming clear – they were thieves.

I started to run after them but it was too late. Somebody shouted, "Stop, thief!" and all of a sudden, a policeman knocked me to the ground and dragged me off to the Court...

Chapter 7

"So that's the story I told to Charley all those years ago. Three months' hard labour in prison, all for something I didn't do. Charley Dickens smiled sadly when I had finished. He just sat back with a faraway look in his eyes."

David, who had listened quietly to his grandfather's story, now sat up straight.

"So what happened to Charley and the Dickens family?" he asked.

"The Dickens family left prison at the same time as I did, after fourteen weeks. John Dickens' mother had just died and left him enough money to pay off his debts. So he was right, something did turn up, after all," replied David's grandad.

"As for his son, Charley, well, how was I to know that he would become the great writer, Charles Dickens?

Looking back, I now realize that even then he was forming stories in his head about the people he met, even me. As you know, David, he died four years ago, in 1870. But his characters will never die, they'll live forever. Tiny Tim and Scrooge, Pip and Little Dorrit, David Copperfield and Nicholas Nickleby, Mr Micawber and Mr Pickwick. Then, there are the characters that I told young Charley about: Fagin, Mr Bumble and the Artful Dodger...

"...Then there's me. Have you guessed the name he gave me?"

"Grandad," said David, "you must be Oliver Twist!"

"That's right. Thanks to Charles Dickens, I am Oliver Twist, the little boy who asked for more."

David looked at his grandad with shining eyes.

"May I ask for more, Grandad?" he said.

The old man laughed, "That depends on what it is."

"More books by Charles Dickens, please!"

Glossary

apprentice a young person learning a trade. In Victorian times, they usually worked for five years, for very little money.

beadle the name given to the man who ran the workhouse in Victorian times.

debtor a person who owes something to someone else, usually money.

gruel oatmeal boiled in water, like porridge.

hard labour a type of punishment in Victorian times, involving heavy work, such as lifting and carrying.

Industrial Revolution rapid development of industry that took place in Britain in the second half of the eighteenth century and first half of the nineteenth. During this time, most of the working population changed from working in the countryside on farms to working in factories in towns.

oakum loose fibre collected by picking old rope to pieces.

Poor Law a law first introduced by Queen Elizabeth I in the sixteenth century to support the poor. It was used throughout the Victorian period.

sevenpence-halfpenny a unit of money in Victorian times. Sevenpence-halfpenny is roughly the equivalent of three pence today.

snuffbox a box containing powdered tobacco. Popular among men in the nineteenth century, snuff was taken up the nose.

terraced a row of houses all joined to each other, with no passages to separate them.

undertaker a person who makes arrangements for funerals.

workhouse a place where very poor people were housed and made to work.

Victorian times the period of time when Victoria was queen of England, from 1837–1901.